Marx and the Climate Crisis

Elaine Graham-Leigh

COUNTERFIRE

Marx and the Climate Crisis

First published in Great Britain in 2020 by Counterfire,
Bow House, 157 Bow Road, London E3 2SE.
Cover design and layout: Feyzi Ismail

ISBN 978-1-907899-11-9

A catalogue record for this book is available from the British
Library.

Printed and bound in Great Britain.
www.counterfire.org

Contents

Chapter One: Facing the climate crisis

The youth strikes for the climate and Extinction Rebellion have between them garnered an impressive amount of mainstream attention for the climate emergency we're facing. They have also made clear that climate breakdown is a systemic, not an individual problem, requiring systemic rather than individual solutions.

Much of the green movement has of course long understood this. 'System change not climate change' was after all the slogan of the demonstrations at the international climate talks in Copenhagen in 2009 and has figured prominently on many other climate protests since. It is also true, however, that the idea that reductions in greenhouse gas emissions should come from people making changes to their personal lifestyles has at times had considerable traction within the green movement. This traction has come both from a sense that carbon emissions are at base caused by individuals and from an understanding of supply and demand which places consumer choices at the centre. Chris Goodall summed up the approach neatly in his *How to Live a Low-carbon Life* in 2007:

> *The threat of climate change requires each of us to take personal responsibility for reducing our impact on the planet's atmosphere. Individually, of course, we are powerless; but our actions influence those around us. Eventually, private companies will perceive a market for low-carbon products, and governments will come to see that real action on climate change is not electorally disastrous.*[1]

The problem with this view is that it fails to understand how individual choices are shaped and constrained by the system in which they are made. Contrary to neoliberal ideology, we are not simply rational consumers, making the most individually beneficial choices in a free market. We are social actors, doing the best we can in situations where we often have little choice at all. If, for example, you work in an out-of-town distribution centre and your shift starts at 4am, your public-transport options for your commute are going to be limited. Casting individual carbon footprints as a personal choice may enable those who have more control over the conditions of their lives to look down on those who don't. It does little to change the underlying problem.

The justification for focusing on individuals has often been a counsel of despair: governments and corporations are not going to act, so the only thing left is personal action. A conclusion that individual action is the only way forward is an acceptance that we have no power to force governments and corporations to act in the way that we would like. It is effectively an argument that the system cannot be changed. This, unsurprisingly, is an understanding of the situation with which many of these governments and corporations have been quite happy. As climate scientist Michael Mann commented recently, we know that the fossil-fuel industry has funded 'deflection campaigns', which are 'aimed to divert attention from big polluters and place the burden on individuals.' Instead, Mann argues, 'we need systemic changes that will reduce everyone's carbon footprint, whether or not they care.'[2]

The scale of the youth climate strikes in particular has now made the argument that individual changes are all we can do seem less like realism than defeatism. When we have four million young people striking worldwide for system change to address the climate crisis, the idea that we can force government action seems much more plausible to many more people than it did only a year ago. Agreeing that system change is what we need is however only a first step.

In some versions of system change, it can become simply a way of enforcing the individual choices which people are perceived to be too slow or too unwilling to adopt without compulsion. For Animal Rebellion, an offshoot of Extinction Rebellion, for example, system change is not a different strategy from individual lifestyle changes but a way to compel these, by legislating to mandate plant-based diets. Moving away from consumer culture to a culture in which people are discouraged from acquiring material possessions to excess (whatever the definition of 'excess' is) can also appear as a goal in some versions of 'system change', despite the fact that this is essentially about changing individual buying behaviour.

This is not to say of course that all calls for system change are similarly limited in scope to mandating changes to individual lifestyles. From the technological Utopias of futurists like Aaron Bastani[3] to the vision of half-Earthers like E O Wilson,[4] who envisage an Earth with restricted human habitation, there is no shortage of calls for fundamental changes to address the environmental crisis. Are humans the enemy of biodiversity, so that it can only thrive in our absence, as the half-Earthers believe, or can we regard nature as a series of natural inputs to be used, sustainably and carefully, as we want? These represent profoundly different views of what human society should look like, yet they are both proposed as systemic changes in response to the same problem. A call for system change plainly is the beginning, not the end of the conversation.

The wide differences in approach to system change are reflected in the range of ideas proposed for how it could be achieved. There can be tendency for green critiques of the system to end up calling for withdrawal from it, whether that is in some aspects of our lives, like getting their electricity through the local co-op rather than from a power company, or completely. This is an idea with a considerable pedigree, being very similar to the beliefs of the late-eighteenth and early-nineteenth-century Utopian Socialists like Saint-Simon, Fourier and Robert Owen. The Utopians believed that setting up communities run along socialist lines would set a powerful enough example that even the ruling class would wish to follow it. As Marx put it in the *Communist Manifesto*, 'they reject all political, and especially all revolutionary, action; they wish to attain their ends by peaceful means, and endeavour, by small experiments, necessarily doomed to failure, and by the force of example, to pave the way for the new social Gospel.'[5]

Both Marx and Engels were sympathetic to the Utopians, but pointed out that it was a belief which arose from a very early stage of industrial capitalism, when people were beginning to be horrified at the conditions suffered by the working class but had not yet understood the proletariat's unique potential for class struggle. In the two hundred years since the Utopians provided their examples of how society could be constructed differently, we have had plenty of proof that capitalism can in fact work perfectly well with small groups of people attempting to withdraw from it. It is not that these attempts are bad ideas in themselves, but that they do not bring down capitalism simply by existing. Nor do they, in themselves, effect any kind of transformation of the system.

What is needed here is clarity about why the current system is so destructive of the environment. Arguments which see the source of the problem in types of behaviour encouraged by capitalism (acquisitiveness, desire for economic growth, tendency to leap in the car to drive to the end of the road, and so on) ultimately put the blame for the climate crisis on individuals, albeit individuals shaped by the capitalist system. If this was the problem, then the answer would have to lie in changing those individuals' mindsets; indeed, overthrowing the system without doing this would simply result in more of the same. Similarly, if we see the problem as lying in the size of the population the earth has to support under capitalism, changing the system would be secondary to reducing the numbers of people.

Against these ideas, a Marxist understanding of how capitalism is inherently destructive of the environment enables us to see that it is not that human society does not fit on a sustainable planet, but that capitalism as a system is the problem. In some quarters, the idea that we should look to Marx and Engels for ecological thinking is a counterintuitive one. Marx and Engels have been accused of being fundamentally uninterested in ecological issues, anthropocentric in their thinking and wedded to the idea of progress as opposed to sustainability.[6] Socialism, in this view, is inherently un-green, unable to respond to the ecological crisis unless it becomes ecosocialism by moving away from Marx's ideas.[7] In fact, Marx and Engels' ecological thinking is essential for understanding what it really means to call for system change to save the planet.

Chapter Two: The metabolic rift: the inherent destructiveness of capitalism

For Marx, the structure of land ownership and land use under capitalism meant that agriculture was essentially unsustainable. As he set out in volume three of *Capital*:

> *Large landed property reduces the agricultural population to a constantly falling minimum, and confronts it with a constantly growing industrial population crowded together in large cities. It thereby creates conditions which cause an irreparable break in the coherence of social interchange prescribed by the natural laws of life. As a result, the vitality of the soil is squandered, and this prodigality is carried by commerce far beyond the borders of a particular state.*[8]

This is the metabolic rift (a term not used in precisely that form by Marx himself, but coined by John Bellamy Foster to characterise Marx's position). Put simply, the metabolic rift arises when the majority of people and animals are removed from the land that grows the food they live on. In a sustainable system, the nutrients from their waste go back into the soil, replenishing it with the nutrients it loses in producing the food. In industrial capitalism, if most people are moved from the country to the towns, then so is their waste, which is no longer a source of nutrients but a pollution problem. The towns now have to find ways of dealing with the waste, while the countryside has to import fertilisers to maintain the fertility of the soil.

Marx based his understanding of the biological issues behind the metabolic rift on the work of Justus von Liebig. Liebig was an agricultural chemist who was particularly concerned about soil fertility. The eighteenth century had seen a revolution in farming methods, with the development of new machines for threshing, harvesting and so on, and of new animal feeds enabling enormous increases in food production. In England, grain production alone increased by almost 50% between 1760 and 1800.[9] This had been achieved on the back of a programme of enclosure which saw over six million acres of land, equal to about a quarter of the total cultivated land in England, turned from common, open or waste land into private fields.[10] Enclosure, and the difficulty of competing with industrial production and capitalist agriculture, had made it virtually impossible for the rural poor to be self-supporting. Whether they stayed in the countryside or moved to the town, either way they were reliant on wage labour rather than subsistence agriculture to feed themselves. As Marx described the process in *Capital*:

> *The continual emigration to the towns, the continual formation of surplus-population in the country through the concentration of farms, conversion of arable land into pasture, machinery etc, and the continual eviction of the agricultural population by the destruction of their cottages, go hand in hand.*[11]

The eighteenth and early nineteenth-century changes to the nature of agricultural production enabled enormous short-term increases in production, but at the expense not only of the living standards of the rural poor but also of the fertility of the soil. The new production methods were effective, but the danger was that they were also unsustainable. Replacing the practices of subsistence agriculture had enabled production to increase but had also removed sustainable farming methods which enabled the soil to replenish the nutrients needed to grow future crops. This was, Liebig believed, robbery agriculture: 'a larger amount of crop was achieved not because the nutrient matters in the soil became richer but because it was based on techniques that make them poorer more quickly.'[12]

Earlier in his career, in the 1840s, Liebig believed that advances in fertilizer technology could replenish the nutrients being taken from the soil by the new agriculture. His own failed experiments with developing nutrient-rich chemical manure convinced him however that this was impossible. By the 1860s, he had come to believe that the only solution to soil depletion was to avoid depleting it in the first place.

Soil fertility and sewage

Both Liebig and Marx saw the urbanisation which was the creation of the industrial revolution as part of the problem. For Marx, the metabolic rift is therefore part of people's alienation from nature under capitalism.[13] Liebig considered that the solution was to return people to pre-industrial living conditions in the countryside, railing for example against toilets: 'the introduction of water-closets into most parts of England results in the irrecoverable loss of the materials capable of producing food for three and a half million people every year.'[14]

It is true that before the late nineteenth century, urban sewage disposal is a demonstration of potentially useful material becoming a pollutant. It is also true that toilets in private homes had made the problem worse. In London, for example, they meant that households did not use local night soil collectors to take their shit away, but discharged it, untreated, either into the Thames directly or into the smaller rivers like the Fleet and Tyburn that feed into it. As a London resident, Marx would have had first-hand experience of the Great Stink of 1858, when a hot summer made the Thames smell so bad that Parliament considered moving to Oxford or St Albans to get away from 'the stench which arose from the river.'[15] Marx's reference in his 1860 response to Karl Vogt to the 'senseless wastefulness which robs the Thames of its purity and the English soil of its manure'[16] may have been heartfelt.

The Great Stink impelled Parliament to approve Joseph Bazalgette's plan to deal with London's sewage, whence Bazalgette 'enters the pantheon of London's heroes.'[17] Bazalgette's solution did not, however, so much resolve the pollution problem as move it further away from the bourgeoisie in central London. In this sense, London's sewage issues are symbolic of how capitalism creates and deals with pollution: usually by moving it elsewhere for poorer people to live with. London's sewage was still discharged untreated into the Thames, just closer to the estuary where it could be washed out to sea. In 1878, when the steamboat *Princess Alice* sank in the Thames Estuary just downstream from the sewage outfall, several people died as a result of being poisoned by the sewage-filled water. The introduction of sewage treatment has of course improved the situation since then, although, alarmingly, 'combined sewer overflows' when heavy rain means that untreated sewage flows straight into the Thames, still happen about 50 times a year.[18] There had been a proposal before Bazalgette to 'preserve the sewage [from London] for Agricultural purposes' by sending it into storage tanks rather than into the Thames, but this idea was rejected by Parliament.[19]

The nature of the specific problem is not quite that the rural poor moved to the towns. While the growth of London's population was clearly a factor in the increasing sewage pollution of its water courses, the growth in water closets was among the wealthier inhabitants, not among the recently displaced rural poor. The Great Stink was the stink of bourgeois shit. It is also true that while there is potential for using treated human waste as fertiliser, this is inadvisable for untreated waste as this would be a major vector in disease transmission.

There are of course attempts to develop composting toilets as a replacement for the water closet model, not least because modern toilets are significant users of clean water.[20] Attempts to close this specific element of the metabolic rift are clearly welcome, but we should not stop there. It is also worth noting at this point that addressing the metabolic rift solely by individuals changing their toilets would be to attempt to address a structural problem through individual action rather than at the structural level. The importance of the metabolic rift is not that it identifies a specific waste disposal issue, but that it demonstrates how capitalist agriculture is inherently unsustainable. This unsustainability has not just local but international consequences.

Imperialism and the guano wars

One effect, as Marx described, is the increasing import of agricultural products and raw materials to the centres of capital from the periphery. Thus, for example, Ireland was 'only an agricultural district of England, marked off by a wide channel from the country to which it yields corn, wool, cattle, industrial and military recruits.'[21] The English stripping of Irish resources amounted to a form of colonial metabolic rift, as Marx made clear in a footnote to this passage: 'it must not be forgotten that for a century and a half England has indirectly exported the soil of Ireland, without as much as allowing its cultivators the means for making up the constituents of the soil that had been exhausted.'[22] In the eyes of English capitalists, Ireland's 'true destiny [was] that of an English sheep-walk and cattle-pasture',[23] so discussions of the 'problem' of Irish overpopulation were in reality justifications for the removal of the people from the land. The shift to capitalist agriculture in Ireland and consequent depopulation, Marx argued, had a direct effect on fertility of the soil:

The land has been underfed and overworked, partly by the injudicious consolidation of farms, and partly because under corn-acre the farmer in a great measure trusted to his labourers to manure the land for them.[24]

The result of English exploitation was therefore 'gradual expulsion of the natives, gradual deterioration and exhaustion of the source of national life, the soil.'[25]

The English colonial occupation of Ireland enabled England to ameliorate the consequences of the metabolic rift by importing Irish agricultural produce, while simultaneously creating a metabolic rift in Ireland. A similar process can be seen at work in attempts to overcome soil exhaustion through the importation of fertilizer. Liebig had found that it was difficult to create an effective chemical fertilizer for mass production, but for robbery agriculture, there were other sources of fertilization available.

Guano (bird shit) can be a particularly good fertiliser as it tends to be high in nitrates, particularly when it is deposited in a dry climate where there is little rain to wash the nutrients away. In the nineteenth century, the world's best guano deposits were on the Chincha Islands off the coast of Peru. The seas around the islands were home to a large anchovy population and the seabirds that fed on them had, over thousands of years, built up guano mountains hundreds of feet high.[26] The guano trade with Peru was dominated by British capitalists, with a British firm, Antony Gibbs & Sons, holding the contract with the Peruvian government for the exclusive right to sell guano on the world market. This did not mean that other powers could not participate, however. In the 1850s, a British officer on a ship off the Chincha Islands watched a hundred ships from 11 countries loading guano there.[27]

The guano rush of the mid-nineteenth century has all the hallmarks of capitalism at its most destructive.

Competition over control of the guano led to two wars (the Chincha Islands War of 1864-1866, in which Peru, Ecuador, Chile and Bolivia fought Spain and the War of the Pacific of 1879-1883, which was Peru versus Chile and Bolivia) and the annexation by the US of 94 islands around the world in search of alternative guano supplies.

Conditions for the workers on the guano were horrific. Most were Chinese workers, who were deceived or straight up forced into being shipped to Peru by European merchants and who were effectively enslaved. As a contemporary described, 'no hell has ever been conceived… that can be equalled in the fierceness of its heat, the horror of its stink, and the damnation of those compelled to labour there, to a deposit of Peruvian guano when being shovelled into ships.'[28] Another contemporary writer noted that few of the Chinese workers survived for more than a few months.

Eventually, the guano trade proved unsustainable. The guano was being removed at a far faster rate than it was deposited, a problem compounded by the way that the guano ships accidentally or sometimes even deliberately drove the seabirds away. This pattern was repeated with other guano deposits, like those on the west coast of Africa, which were exploited in the nineteenth century as an alternative to the superior Peruvian guano. In the late twentieth and early twenty-first century, as demand for guano started to rise as it was seen as an organic fertiliser, overfishing virtually wiped out the Peruvian anchovies on which the seabirds lived, so that their population has fallen from around 60 million in the nineteenth-century to about four million now. The guano deposits are now in some places only about a foot deep.[29]

The nineteenth-century guano trade is an effective demonstration of the metabolic rift and all destruction and suffering that capitalist exploitation entails. The guano trade ended in the early twentieth century when Fritz Haber developed the Haber Process, a nitrogen fixation process which allows industrial production of ammonia from atmospheric nitrogen. This obviated the need to remove nutrients from one part of the world to replenish depleted soils in another. It did not however overcome the metabolic rift in agriculture so much as change its nature. Industrial agricultural processes still lead to soil depletion and the fertiliser brought in to make up for this still causes a pollution problem. Nitrates in agricultural fertiliser end up as pollutants in water sources, which has serious implications for biodiversity in rivers and streams. In 2018, a House of Commons Environmental Audit Committee commented that it was a serious concern that 86% of English rivers could not be awarded a good ecological status in 2016 because of nitrate pollution.[30]

Capital's destructive mobility

The agricultural metabolic rift here arises because of capitalist industrial agricultural production, so it could be concluded that the essential problem is the industrialisation, rather than capitalism *per se*. This could then lead to two, alternative conclusions: that capitalism can be made to be sustainable with better technologies for production, or that a non-capitalist society would have to abandon industrialisation and the living standards that go with it.

Marx was very clear, however, that capitalism's environmental destructiveness is inherent to the system. The depletion of the soil by capitalist agricultural practises is the same process as the exploitation of the workers. As he wrote in *Capital*, for example:

> Capital cares nothing for the length of life of labour-power. All that concerns it is simply and solely the maximum of labour-power, that can be rendered fluent in a working-day. It attains this end by shortening the extent of the labourer's life, as a greedy farmer snatches increased produce from the soil by robbing it of its fertility.[31]

Squeezing out the last drop of profit from the land, like squeezing every bit of possible labour power from the workforce, is not a failure of technology or knowledge of sustainability. In capitalism, it is the point.

That it is capitalism, rather than simply the form of technology used, which is destructive of the environment, can be seen from the fact that the hallmarks of capitalist destructiveness existed before industrialisation. The typical pattern of exploitation to destruction of a new natural resource demonstrated in the guano rush can be found centuries before in early capitalist production, for example in the central European mining boom of around 1450-1550.[32] Capitalism's ability to create the industrial revolution gave it scope to drive environmental destruction on a far greater scale, but industrialisation is destructive because it is capitalist, not because environmental devastation would always have to be inherent to any kind of industrialisation, whether capitalist or not.

Part of capital's destructive capability is the way in which capitalists do not have to stick around to deal with the consequences of the destruction their production causes. While it is obviously the case that non-capitalist societies have managed to destroy their environment as well (by deforestation, failure to maintain irrigation systems etc), where ruling class power is indivisible from the possession of particular natural resources, like productive land, if those natural resources are abused too far, they can no longer act as sources of power. Feudal lords, rulers of ancient states and so on had therefore a built-in need to pay at least minimal attention to sustainability (even if they would not have recognised the term). Capitalists however have no such requirement.

Individual capitalists can invest in extremely destructive types of production, make money and move on to invest in something else. There is no inherent need for them to care about the prospect of resource depletion or environmental damage, as long as they can get their investment out before those particular chickens come home to roost. A demonstration of this is the fate of the British firm, Antony Gibbs & Sons, which held the guano monopoly from the Peruvian government in the mid-nineteenth century. Their success was undamaged by the consequences of the exploitation of the guano, or indeed of the Chinese workers enslaved to extract it. By the 1880s, they had moved out of guano harvesting and into nitrate of soda production for munitions. In the twentieth century they moved again into banking and insurance, a sector in which they remained a player until they were taken over in 1981. The company was formally wound up in 2007 but still effectively forms the basis of HSBC's insurance-broking arm.[33] The guano may be gone, but the effects of the surplus value generated from it remain.

While it is the nature of capitalism rather than industrialisation alone which lies behind the metabolic rift, it is of course true that industrial production enabled capitalism to cause environmental destruction on such an increased scale that this has to be regarded as a qualitative, not just a quantitative shift. The scale of capitalism and the requirement for ever-increasing profits is indeed a significant part of the system's innate destructive capability. When considering capitalism and the environment, we have to talk about growth.

Chapter Three: The question of green growth

The growth of the global economy is seen by many to be a significant contributor to environmental damage under capitalism. As for example Tim Jackson, then Economics Commissioner for the Sustainable Development Commission, argued in 2009:

> *This extraordinary ramping up of global economic activity [in the second half of the twentieth century] has no historical precedent. It's totally at odds with our scientific knowledge of the finite resource base and the fragile ecology on which we depend for survival. And it has already been accompanied by the degradation of an estimated 60% of the world's ecosystems.*[34]

In some ways, the association of growth and ecological destruction is simply an expression of the scale of capitalism compared to other modes of production. As discussed, it is not that environmental damage is unknown in other economic systems, but that capitalism's capacity for production and for damage caused by that production is so much greater that this becomes a qualitative rather than just a quantitative difference. Economic growth under capitalism is then an intensifier of capitalist ecological harm. If production under capitalism is damaging, then more production will obviously be more so.

This may seem straightforward, but the identification of growth as a key danger for the environment under capitalism has given rise to a number of areas of debate. The first of these is the question of whether it is possible to have 'green' growth. Can capitalist economies keep the growth bit, but ditch the environmental destruction that goes with it?[35]

Is green growth possible?

For a start, it is clear that many productive operations can be made more environmentally friendly. Just as the technology exists now to cut greenhouse-gas emissions from homes and personal transport, so too can businesses get their power from renewable energy generation, switch from plastics to using recycled or recyclable materials, make it possible for their staff to use public transport, and so on. They can even fight for green infrastructure so that, for example, they could move freight by rail rather than road. In some senses, then, since it would obviously be possible to reduce the greenhouse-gas impacts of daily activities, it should therefore be possible to expand those activities without damaging the environment. Indeed, a recent study reported that green growth did appear to have been achieved by some Scandinavian countries.[36]

The concern though is that driving GDP growth would inevitably mean more consumer spending, which in turn necessitates more production of consumer goods, more resource use, more freight transport and so on. Even with the obvious changes to power generation and transport infrastructure, the argument goes, it would be difficult to prevent this from increasing greenhouse-gas emissions, and it would also increase depletion of all sorts of natural resources. So, is it possible to have growth without goods?

The idea that green growth is possible if spending were to be shifted to spending on non-material things has become popular in some quarters in recent years. Think, for example, of the now regular media features advising us to give 'experiences' rather than physical things as greener gifts.[37] Some, such as the anti-environmentalists Ted Nordhaus and Michael Shellenberger, argue that a transition to a 'postmaterialist' economy would be a natural result of prosperity,[38] while others believe that it would only come about through conscious 'self-limitation'.[39] Either way, however, the problem with a belief in non-material growth is in identifying genuinely non-material services for there to be growth in.

The examples often used at this point in pre-internet discussions are personal care services like hairdressing, nail bars and the like. It is difficult to see these sorts of services as genuinely non-material, however, leaving aside whether it would really be possible to base an entire economy on their consumption. It is true that the customer in these cases does not automatically leave the shop carrying a purchase in a plastic bag, but these are still services which usually use products (shampoo, nail varnish, dye, etc) and which take place in material premises which have to be heated, lit and so on.

For more recent discussions, the obvious examples are services delivered online, but here there are the same sorts of difficulties. An online purchase may appear immaterial to the end consumer, but they are still accessing it on a very material device. The online service itself is also hosted somewhere in the world on a very material server in a server farm in (probably) a concrete warehouse. All of these devices use resources for their manufacture and a considerable amount of power for their operation. It was estimated in 2017 that by 2020, the internet would account for 3.5% of global greenhouse-gas emissions.[40]

The issues with coming up with a plausible model for non-material consumption and growth lead to an alternative strategy. If we cannot have growth without resource use and environmental damage, can we have capitalism without growth? The idea that capitalism does not have to mean continual growth has been around since John Stewart Mill, who theorised that the capitalist economy would grow only until it reached a 'stationary state.' This was developed in the twentieth century by Herman Daly into the steady-state theory. This posits an economy neither growing nor going into recession, with constant labour and capital and therefore constant flows of goods and services produced. As long as the level of goods and services produced is set at a sustainable level, there should therefore be no reason for the system to overstep its bounds in the future.[41]

Daly did not believe that it would be possible to divert growth into non-material production to get around resource constraints, famously commenting that if you're facing a shortage of wood, you can't make up for it by employing more carpenters. The steady state was an attempt to offer an alternative, by proposing a society where rather than decoupling materials and growth, the decoupling was between growth and capitalism. In order to do so, however, the steady-state theory has to regard growth as inessential for capitalism.

Demand and supply, or supply and demand?

This view of growth has become influential, to the extent that it is easy to find plenty of examples in the mainstream media of interest in economic growth being portrayed as if it were a personal foible of late twentieth and early twenty-first century Westerners.[42] Concern for GDP growth is 'a fixation', 'a delusion' or 'an obsession'; something that we need to learn that we can set aside. This view of insistence on growth as a collective misunderstanding of what is good for us sees its political prominence as coming from popular demand. Politicians promise us economic growth, in this view, because we demand it. And why do we demand it? The answers to this one vary, but seem to circle around the general idea that it is something to do with a collective obsession with stuff. If we would all just stop wanting to buy so many things, and therefore insisting that politicians enable us to carry on doing so, then a steady state might be possible. We should, in fact, 're-embrace such notions as thrift, frugality and self-reliance'[43] or, at the very least, 'self-limitation'.[44]

The most obvious rejoinder to this line of argument is that it is easier for people in relatively prosperous situations to enthuse about the joys of not consuming than it is for those who don't know where the money for their basic needs is going to come from. Deriding others' obsession with GDP growth comes easier to those who don't have to fear losing their job in a downturn. As Marx noted, capitalists have long been enthusiastic proponents of self-restraint for their workers; after all, if they would just limit their consumption, they could manage on their low wages. 'Society today' Marx wrote, 'makes the paradoxical demand that he for whom the object of exchange is subsistence should deny himself, not he for whom it is wealth.'[45] In Marx's view, against this pressure from the capitalist class that workers should 'maintain themselves as pure labouring machines', 'the worker's participation in the higher, even cultural satisfactions, the agitation for his own interests, newspaper subscriptions, attending lectures, educating his children, developing his taste etc [is] his only share of civilisation which distinguishes him from the slave.'[46]

Given this framework, it is reasonable to regard modern calls for others to practice self-restraint in consumption with a certain amount of suspicion. There are also fundamental problems with the view that capitalism could reach and maintain a steady state. The first of these is the way that the steady-state theory is based on an assumption that demand leads supply. Goods are produced because people want them. If they can become enlightened enough to turn away from consumption, then the production will also go away. If they merely choose another sort of consumption, then production will follow that, too.

It is this assumption which leads some commentators to treat changes in production as the result of consumer foibles, such as in this recent comment on youth consumption: 'Young people may stop buying cars, but they buy resource intensive iPhones every two years and take Uber and Lyft more than they use the bus.'[47] Not only is this not true for the majority of young people, it also manages to ignore the structure of capitalism in which the apparently free choices to upgrade a phone and call an Uber take place. From the planned obsolescence of mobile phones, to concerted campaigns of ride-sharing apps to encourage people to use them rather than public transport, these are not choices being made in a vacuum. It is not that consumers were demanding a new minicab company with a nice app but terrible employment practices; the supply here created the apparent demand.

Marx was very clear that, despite the assumptions of bourgeois economists, while workers' ability to consume is important to capitalists, production is not created by their demand, which would never be sufficient to generate profits from production.[48] It follows therefore that if a particular level of production is not determined by consumer demand, then neither is the need for growth. Regarding calls for economic growth as a foible of the ignorant at best is to ignore the very real suffering economic downturns cause, and at worst is to misunderstand the fundamentals of capitalism.

Capitalism as a dynamic system

Capitalism is not 'obsessed with' growth because particular capitalists believe that continual growth is essential, any more than we are dependent on oil as a result of individuals' continued car ownership. Growth is part of the structure of capitalism; indeed, without continued expansion, capitalism does not work at all. Capitalism is not a static but a dynamic system, which works only on the basis of ever-increasing profits. Competition between capitalist businesses impels each to seek expansion to outdo their competitors – the drive to greater and greater accumulation – but the profits generated by this are effectively dead capital if they cannot themselves be invested in a way that will get the capitalist a compound return on their investment. It is this underlying dynamic in capitalism which drives the cycles of boom and bust, expansion and depression which have become familiar. These aren't a malfunction of capitalism but simply a result of how the system works.

Because the need for growth arises from the need for competitive advantage, an explicit belief or not in the value of growth within the system will not change it: even chief executives who talk the talk on green issues are still looking for ways to become more profitable than the other businesses in their industries, and to beat them to new areas into which to expand. Industrialisation comes in here because mechanised production initially allows those capitalists who adopt it to produce larger quantities of products more cheaply than their competitors, although it also contains the seeds of the next cyclical 'bust' by causing the rate of profit to decline. Marx showed how this happens as companies invest their profits, i.e. the surplus value produced by the labour of their workforces, in machinery which replaces labour. This therefore reduces the only factor which produces new value. As the rate of profit falls, this produces a crisis which destroys many capitals and enables a rise in profitability, and so a new round of expansion. This then lasts until the next cycle when many businesses in a sector collapse, and their surviving rivals improve their rates of profit by eating the corpses.

This underlying dynamic means that growth cannot be edited out of the capitalist system, which can only survive through finding continual opportunities to expand. For resource extraction this can be expansion into literal new areas, thus providing a motor for imperialism, or changes to the nature of production to allow capitalist market relations to enter previous uncommodified sectors. An example of the latter is the Green Revolution, a development programme for higher-yield crops in the 1960s – 1990s, which effectively marketized what was previously subsistence agriculture.[49] Without these possibilities for expansion, capitalism is in trouble. In the agricultural sector, they enable capitalist agricultural production to overcome the declining rate of profit and the effects of the metabolic rift, as Marx and Engels were well aware. Engels for example remarked in 1865 that it was the possibility of expansion to the West which was coming to the rescue of US agricultural production. 'If all these regions have been ploughed up and after that shortage sets in, then will be the time to say *caveat consules*.' (trans: Let the consuls, [rulers of the Roman republic] beware.)[50]

That the environmental damage caused by capitalism is structural, not a result of consumer demand or individual views on growth, is also demonstrated by the timing of the most significant increases in greenhouse-gas emissions. As Ian Angus has recently pointed out, while greenhouse-gas emissions have been accumulating since the Industrial Revolution, there was a significant increase not just in emissions themselves but also in species and forest loss, acidification, biosphere degradation and so on from the mid-twentieth century on.[51] This intensification of environmental destructiveness therefore came about directly after the end of the Second World War. This was not a coincidence. The US victory in the Second World War created the conditions for the enrichment of US capitalists and for the current climate crisis: 'a powerful industrial base in the United States, concentrated in a few hundred giant corporations and dominated by the petroleum/automotive sector; a large and growing military budget; a disciplined and financially secure labor force, purged of militants and militancy; and a seemingly infinite supply of cheap energy.'[52]

The lesson of the Second World War was of the centrality of control of oil supplies to success in modern warfare. The Allies may not have won had they not been able to cut off German access to oil and to maintain it for themselves. This made oil a central military priority, and also cemented the dominant position of the petroleum/automotive sector in the US. These were preconditions for a system dependent on greenhouse-gas emitting technologies for military and domestic production. Modern imperialist wars are therefore both a result of the need to maintain a hegemony which is inherently environmentally destructive and a source in themselves of ecological damage.

The US military admits to getting through 395,000 barrels of oil every day, including jet-fuel consumption which makes it the single largest consumer in the world. This is an astonishing figure which is nevertheless likely to be a considerable underestimate. Once all the oil use from military contractors, weapons manufacturing and all those secret bases and operations that get missed out of the official figures are factored in, the real daily usage is likely to be closer to a million barrels.[53] The US military emits around 5% of the world's greenhouse-gas emissions from its infrastructure; more when it is engaged in combat. The Iraq War is estimated to have produced around 141 million metric tonnes of CO2 between 2003 and 2007.[54]

The damage capitalism causes to the environment is therefore at a structural level, not at the level of consumer choice. If growth cannot be made immaterial, nor edited out of capitalism by changing people's minds, this then emphasises that capitalism is inherently ecologically destructive. The mechanisms by which it damages the environment are inbuilt; while they can be overcome temporarily, or for specific environmental problems, the tendency to destruction cannot be edited out. This is not however the end of the debate. The destructiveness of activities within the capitalist mode of production might not, in some views, be capitalism's fault. How can we be sure that a different economic structure would not produce the same effects?

Chapter Four: Natural limits and carrying capacity

Discussions of the environmental damage caused by capitalism in general, and economic growth under capitalism specifically, often counterpose the concepts of growth and natural limits. You can't have infinite growth on a finite planet, we are told. Interpreted as a logical proposition, this contains a kernel of obvious truth. If you use natural resources at a rate greater than their rate of replacement, eventually you will run out. As a statement of principle, it works most clearly, however, when thinking about numbers of people and physical space. There is clearly a finite amount of land on the planet, so logically there must be a maximum number of land-dwelling creatures who can physically fit on it. The question is not so much whether that is true as an abstract proposition, but whether it is a useful way of thinking about natural limits to production.

It is of course the case that natural limits would be very much more complex than simply the land surface of the planet. Any understanding of limits has to encompass not simply natural resource availability but also the environmental elements that make the planet liveable. The Stockholm Resilience Centre's definition of nine planetary boundaries attempts to do this, including climate, biodiversity and soil fertility among others.[55] The question for example of how much food can be produced is not simply how much land there is that could be used for growing crops, but how much land could be so used within a sustainable system that also addressed deforestation, extinction, greenhouse-gas emissions, etc.

The Stockholm Resilience Centre concludes that of its nine planetary boundaries, three are currently being breached. This is an expression of the environmental damage caused under capitalism as a result of the inherent destructiveness of the system, but for some, it is also an expression of a fundamental truth that natural limits would affect whatever economic system we had. This is the concept of the carrying capacity of the planet: that human numbers can and have exceeded the capacity of the world to sustain them. In this view, the real environmental issue facing us is that there are simply too many people. Capitalism makes this situation worse through unsustainable production methods, but the underlying problem would be there in a more sustainable system as well.

This idea underlies the popular trope of a billion people worldwide starving while another billion are overweight. Many versions of this do make explicit the conclusion that the latter are the cause of the former's situation, as in this early example from 1999, referring to 'the overconsumption of the billion or so who consume far more than their basic needs and, it is reasonable to assume, contribute directly or indirectly to the underconsumption of the impoverished billion.'[56] Whether the implication is explicit or implicit, however, the assumption is the same; that while we can hope that the natural limits of the earth are sufficient, they are limited. We fit within them so snugly that even in a sustainable system, for someone to overconsume, someone else would have to be going without.

The result of this conclusion would have to be that a post-capitalist society would have to be one in which consumption and living standards were strictly limited; a point at which we are usually treated to a paean to the delights of non-material things and the quality of life that low consumption can bring. Indeed, it could be inferred from many discussions of natural limits that the point of overthrowing capitalism would be as a way of introducing and enforcing such limits to consumption. In other words, the real problem is not so much capitalism, as people.

This was not the view of Marx or Engels. As discussed, Marx was a defender of working-class consumption, against capitalists' attempts to limit the costs of the reproduction of their employees' labour and therefore their wages. This was not ignoring unpalatable truths about consumption, but a recognition of the political use of criticism of working-class people's expenditure on anything above the barest subsistence level. It was coupled with an understanding of limits which held that the idea of a fixed, proximate planetary carrying capacity was false. As Engels wrote in his *Outlines of a Critique of Political Economy*, for example, human labour could always extend what might appear to be the natural limits of production: 'the productivity of the land can be infinitely increased by the application of capital, labour and science.'[57]

This type of thinking from Engels and from Marx has seen them dubbed as being Promethean, after the Greek mythological figure who stole fire from the gods. The criticism is that in believing that human technological skill would overcome apparent limits in production had them siding with productivism and the machine 'against nature.'[58] This is, as Bellamy Foster and Burkett have pointed out, a rather unfair caricature of an argument which is very far from being a statement of Man's mastery over Nature. Engels was well aware of the possibility of unintended consequences leading to environmental destruction, writing for example in his *Dialectics of Nature* about how the deforestation of the lower slopes of the Italian Alps had unforeseen effects on soil erosion and flooding. His point was not that humans should expect to be able to control the natural world, far from it, but that humanity has 'the advantage of all other creatures of being able to learn its laws and apply them correctly.'[59]

Malthus and natural limits to population

This correct application of natural laws patently does not happen within capitalism. Whether that means it could happen at all is the crux of the argument about natural limits, which can only be understood in the context of its history. The concept of natural limits goes back to Thomas Malthus, whose *Principle of Population* relies on the assumption that there is a fixed limit to the numbers of people who can be supported. As he argued for example in the preface to the second edition, 'through the animal and vegetable kingdoms Nature has scattered the seeds of life abroad with the most profuse and liberal hand; but has been comparatively sparing in the room and the nourishment necessary to rear them.'[60] Malthus' central argument was that these natural limits were what was responsible for the poor starving; this was 'a great restrictive law' from which 'man cannot by any efforts of reason escape'.[61]

Malthus was writing at the very end of the eighteenth century and the beginning of the nineteenth: the first edition of the *Principle of Population* was published in 1798 and the second edition in 1803. It has been argued that his conclusions were correct for non-industrial societies, but were invalidated by the Industrial Revolution and the great advances in agricultural production seen in his lifetime in the late eighteenth and early nineteenth centuries. He was, it has been claimed, 'a clear-headed theoretician of traditional societies, but he was a prophet of the past; he was born too late in a world too new'.[62] Marx and Engels' belief in human technological capabilities often seems to be seen in this context, as part of an argument that industrial technological developments under capitalism invalidate and will always overcome concern about natural limits.

Given capitalism's destructiveness of the environment

and the malign consequences of efforts like the Green Revolution to expand agricultural production further, it is reasonable to regard assertions that industrial capitalism will always find the solution to apparent natural limits with some scepticism. The point here though is that this was never Marx and Engels' argument. Their view was, rather, that the human capacity to learn and labour on their environment meant that it would be possible for a non-capitalist system to organise production sustainably and fairly.

On the question of whether the logical natural limits of the planet are relevant, a Marxist view would therefore be that while they are clearly relevant for capitalism, this does not mean that a socialist society would find itself in a similar position without stringent limits to individual living standards. The alternative position, that we would be up against natural limits under any economic and political system because of our numbers, is in the curious position of simultaneously relegating capitalist production to an exacerbating factor and elevating the operation of capitalism to the level of a natural law. This is brought out clearly by Marx and Engels in their writings against Malthus.

In essence, Malthus' theory of population was 'an apology for the condition of the working people, and a warning against all attempts to ameliorate the condition of society.' Its political use alone as a justification for the punitive 1834 Poor Law would have led Marx and Engels to oppose it as 'a welcome gift to the industrial bourgeoisie.'[63] Engels called it 'the most open declaration of war of the bourgeoisie on the proletariat.'[64] Marx and Engels took issue however not only with the political conclusions drawn from Malthus' work but with his conflation of capitalism and nature.

Capitalism as natural process
Malthus argued that the poor starved because there were simply too many of them. This was true, he believed, even when they were dependent on wage labour rather than

subsistence farming for survival, so that unemployment itself became for Malthus a natural phenomenon like soil depletion or crop failure. In the second edition of the *Principle of Population*, he described anyone unable to support themselves as being rejected by nature, not just the capitalist employer: 'At nature's mighty feast there is no cover for him. She tells him to begone.'[65]

Malthus here was casting as a natural process capitalism's need for a reserve army of labour: unemployed workers who can be taken on temporarily to respond to times of high demand for manufacturing output. These workers, as Engels pointed out, made up 'the "surplus population" of England, which keeps body and soul together by begging, stealing, street-sweeping, collecting manure, pushing handcarts, driving donkeys, peddling, or performing occasional small jobs.' Their lack of permanent means of employment was confused by Malthus with a lack of the means of subsistence, because Malthus did not want to see the operation of capitalist society as anything other than naturally ordained.

It is of course clear that it makes no sense to talk about unemployment as a natural process, any more than it was a natural process that enclosed common land in the eighteenth and nineteenth centuries and impoverished the rural working class. The poor whom Malthus was imagining being banished from nature's table were not starving because there was an absolute lack of resources to feed them, as both Marx and Engels pointed out. Enclosure and capitalist agriculture rather had deprived them of the resources to feed themselves, so they had to fall back on low-paid, intermittent wage labour. This was a point made vividly by William Cobbett, writing in 1830 about the poor of the Avon valley. He commented that the population of the area seemed to have fallen compared to earlier periods, but that the people who remained seemed to be no less poor. 'Where, then' he asked 'is their natural tendency to increase beyond the means of subsistence for them? Beyond, indeed, the means of that sustenance with which a system like this will leave them.'[66]

Malthus' error in viewing economic and political phenomena as natural law indicates a fundamental problem with much of the discussion about natural limits, in that it focuses on how those natural limits act on individuals, rather than on societies. In fact, even events like famines, which might seem to be an obvious expression of there being simply too many people for the available food supplies, can be shown to be socially constructed.

The view of Malthus which sees him as only invalidated by industrial agriculture holds that until then, the population would have been pressing on the limits of production, such that any failure of the harvest would mean there were too many mouths to feed and people would starve. This ignores the structural reasons for underproduction in the medieval period, but it also ignores the extent to which famine is not so much a natural phenomenon, unmediated by the mode of production operating in the society in which it occurs, as it is a social one. The number of historical famines in which there appears to have been an absolute dearth of food in a particular area (in other words, that regardless of distribution, there was insufficient food per head to live on) is actually very small. There is one possible example from India in 1344-5, but even that involved a presumably well-fed King organising famine relief for the population, so may not have been a situation of starvation for everyone. As Amartya Sen argues, 'Starvation is the characteristic of some people not *having* enough to eat. It is not the characteristic of there being not enough to eat. While the latter can be the cause of the former, it is but one of many possible causes.'[67]

This is true not only for pre-industrial famines but also for some of the best-known famines of the modern era. The Irish Potato Famine of 1845-51, in which at least one million people died, was caused by potato blight, but also by the way in which the rural poor in Ireland had been limited to smaller and smaller plots, in which potatoes were the only feasible crop. That the issue was not an absolute dearth of food in Ireland is demonstrated by the fact that grain was still being exported from Ireland at the height of the famine.[68] Similarly, the Bengal Famine of 1943 was the result largely of British imperial policies and the deliberate destruction or diversion of food from the area for the war effort.[69]

The reality is that economies and the environment interact at the level of the society, not at the individual level. A society can damage its environment, even suffer collapse because of ecological damage, without that meaning that large numbers of people with a different economic and social system could not live in the area successfully. The Mayan civilisation, for example, is often cited as an example of a society 'operating at the limits of the environment's carrying capacity' which destroyed its environment and fell victim to prolonged drought.[70] While it is clearly the case that the major Mayan cities were abandoned, it is unlikely that, as some have argued, millions of the people died of hunger and thirst as a result. Even while the cities were allowed to fall into ruin, there were still millions of Maya living in the area. It was the Mayan society which could not be accommodated within the natural limits set by the drier climate, not the numbers of people *per se*.[71]

That the capitalist system is destructive of the environment therefore does not indicate that an alternative society with the same size of population would necessarily be so. Marx and Engels' confidence in human ingenuity under a system run rationally for the benefit of all rather than for profit was not necessarily misplaced. Indeed, the development of renewable energy generation as an alternative for fossil fuels is one example of how human ingenuity can develop solutions to environmental problems. The issues we face with climate change are not because we have failed to come up with non-greenhouse-gas emitting alternatives.

Neither Marx nor Engels denied the ways in which capitalism was breaching and would continue to breach the natural limits of sustainable production. They were Promethean in the sense that they did not consider that humanity under a different system would inevitably be up against those same natural limits. The arguments that the same natural limits would always apply, work by taking processes under capitalism as if they are natural and eternal, whereas Marx and Engels were very clear that capitalism is a historical not a natural phenomenon.

Marx and Engels are accused however not only of believing that humans in a rational system would always be able to overcome environmental problems, but of homocentrism. That is, that in their belief in humanity's ability to transform the natural world through labour, they were seeing humanity as masters of the natural world. Their viewpoint put humanity before, and as more important than, nature. This for many green thinkers combines with Marx and Engels' failure to consider the pre-eminence of natural limits to put them on the wrong side of ecological debates; with the smokestacks, rather than with the solar panels, as it were. It is therefore to the Marxist view of nature that we must turn next.

Chapter Five: The natural world and us

In some green thought, a fundamental division is between homocentric and ecocentric views of the natural world; in other words, whether you see human society as of key importance, or whether nature comes first. In this dichotomy, Marx's ecology is often seen as homocentric and therefore by implication stuck in an old fashioned, conservative model of how human society and nature should be viewed. Moving from a Marxist position to an ecocentric one, in this view, would be to move to a more progressive position, embracing 'more radical traditions of green thought that strive for a qualitative transformation in our subjective relation to nature - psychologically, emotionally, aesthetically, cognitively, culturally.'[72]

This may seem a rather abstruse debate, particularly in the context of the immediate, material reality of the climate crisis, but the question of Marx and Engels' homocentrism is an important one. At base, the debate about how we should view human society's relationship to nature is a debate about what that relationship should be. We know that modern capitalist societies have caused untold harm to the natural world, but is that fundamentally because they are capitalist, or because they are human?

This is largely not a debate about immediate measures necessary to safeguard endangered species and habitats in the short term. If, for example, setting aside national park land would enable some species to survive when they would otherwise die out, that would clearly be a good thing. It does not follow however that the type of actions appropriate now to ameliorate some of the worst damage caused under capitalism tells us much about what our relationship to the natural world should be, or could be in a post-capitalist system. Just because in capitalism protecting the natural world seems to necessitate setting aside reservations for it does not itself mean that these reservations would always be needed.

This, then, is another facet of the fundamental question for ecology: is capitalism the problem, or is it humans? Can we posit a post-capitalist human society which would be able to interact sustainably with the natural world, or would the only hope for nature always to be to protect it from us?

Are humans bad for nature?

There is a considerable body of green thought which views the scale and reach of human activity and influence on the natural world as unambiguously a bad thing. In August 2016, the International Geological Congress voted formally to recognise that the world has entered a new geological era, the Anthropocene. The effect of human activity on the planet has now become as significant as that of the meteor that wiped out the dinosaurs and ended the Cretaceous era.[73] Crucially, this activity can be expected to have entered the geological record, so future scientists would be able to distinguish rocks, layers in ice cores and so on, laid down in the Holocene from those of the Anthropocene.

There is still considerable debate about the precise factors which mark the transition from the Holocene to the Anthropocene, and about the date, but for some scientists it is at least partly about the sheer scale of human society as well as about the damage caused by more system-specific issues. Paul Crutzen, one of the first to argue for the Anthropocene, for example, cited the ten-fold human population growth in three centuries and the exploitation of 30-50% of the Earth's land surface as factors in the Anthropocene designation.[74]

If the problem for the natural world is the sheer size of human society, rather than the economic and political structures of that society, then clearly changing those structures would not be a solution. The answer would rather have to be that human society must be scaled back to a point where its dimensions were no longer malign. For some, the ideal size of the human population is zero: there are arguments that we should allow ourselves to go extinct for the sake of the planet.[75] Most would not go that far, but even many of those with a less extreme position make an explicit juxtaposition between the natural world and the size of the population. It's not infrequent for those arguing that population growth is an environmental problem to cite the concomitant effects on national parks, for example, as 'the ... wilderness, space, mobility and other intangibles that lose out to crowding and population growth.'[76] The point however is not just about numbers of people, but their distribution. Regardless of the size of the human population, in this view, it has to be compelled to leave space for nature.

Perhaps the most notable current example of this is scientist E O Wilson's half-Earth programme. This is a proposal to 'save our imperilled biosphere' by 'devot[ing] half the surface of the Earth to nature.'[77] In other words, as has also been proposed by deep ecologists like Arne Naess, humans would only be allowed to occupy specific areas, adding up to no more than half of the land surface of the Earth, while the rest of the planet was given over to be untouched wilderness.

E O Wilson's campaign is the most explicit about withdrawing human influence from the Earth on this scale, but proposals for rewilding can tread some of the same ground, albeit in a more modest framework. Tim Flannery, for example, recently proposed a vision of Europe in 2100 in which the cities were islands in a forested wilderness, into which the Europeans would only venture for recreation and adventure.[78] The Rewilding Europe campaign run by several NGOs also makes an explicit call for the removal of human activity from areas to be rewilded: 'we should step back and let nature manage itself.'[79]

These sorts of proposals might at first glance seem to be little more than a souped-up green belt, restricting the development of greenfield land, but in fact they go much further than that. Half-Earthing and rewilding envisage the withdrawal of all human activity, not just urbanisation, from large parts of the Earth's land surface. This includes agriculture; in Flannery's future Europe, for example, food production would happen in belts immediately surrounding the cities, in greenhouses and 'other structures.'[80]

The 'other structures' here are presumably for lab-grown food, which has been enjoying a fair amount of publicity recently as a potential response to the climate crisis.[81] The arguments for lab-grown food are based on the assumption that the only way to save the Earth is to withdraw human activity from it. Agriculture is inescapably damaging and simply has to be abandoned in favour of hi-tech food production. Even farm animals here are part of the destructive human society, so have to be extirpated to make space for wildlife, which presumably here only includes species which have not doomed themselves by collaborating with us.

In this view, then, a saved planet would be a planet on which human influence was corralled into specific areas, leaving the rest of nature human-free. If human activity *per se* is seen as an environmental problem, this might be a necessary if not particularly palatable step. It is possible however to interpret the Anthropocene differently.

Human society as part of nature

While, as noted, some scientists have included human activity and presence in the natural world as a sign of the Anthropocene, by and large the conclusion that we have entered a new geological era is about environmental damage, not simply our existence in the environment. Capitalism has enabled an unparalleled expansion in the effect that human society has had on the planet, but the point is that this effect has been malign. It is the ecological destruction that capitalism has wreaked which has pushed us into the Anthropocene, not simply the numbers of people on the planet. It is worth noting here that one of the most convincing markers of the beginning of the Anthropocene is not associated with the size of human populations or of extent of land use, but of modern warfare. The marker which any future geologists would take as the sign of a new era is the fallout from nuclear weapons testing.[82]

In a Marxist view, capitalism's ability to cause environmental harm does not mean that the only way to protect the natural world in any human system would be to withdraw human society from it. Indeed, positing such a separation between human society and the natural world would fail as an ecological strategy because it would be to perpetuate the very alienation from nature which unpins capitalism's damage to the environment in the first place. The argument that we have to leave nature alone is not only unnecessary and undesirable, it would continue to entrench the relationship to nature which enables its destruction.

Marx and Engels were firm in their rejection of ideas of nature which eschewed a materialist conception of nature for reactionary or sentimental views of 'free nature' with which humanity should be reunited. This was the view of the True Socialists, an influential intellectual movement in Germany before 1848.[83] 'This cult of nature', Marx and Engels wrote in 1850, 'is limited to the Sunday walks of an inhabitant of a small provincial town who childishly wonders at the cuckoo laying its eggs in another bird's nest'.[84] Their point was that nature should not be idealised as a source of spiritual awakening but understood as the material basis for human existence.

This did not mean that human society could be understood separately from the natural world; far from it. Marx and Engels were clear that humans are a part of nature. Nature, Marx wrote in his *Economic and Philosophical Manuscripts*, is humanity's 'inorganic body', as much part of us as our organic, human bodies: 'To say that man's physical and mental life is linked to nature simply means that nature is linked to itself, for man is a part of nature.'[85] In this way, Marx and Engels saw nature and human society as existing in a dialectical relationship. As Engels argued, relations in nature proceed in dialectical ways just as much as relations in human society do:

> *Nature is the test of dialectics, and it must be said for modern natural science that it has furnished extremely rich and daily increasing materials for this test, and has thus proved that in the last analysis Nature's process is dialectical and not metaphysical.*[86]

Dialectics are not imposed on the natural world in Marxist thought, they arise from it. It follows that the conventional view of human society and the natural world as two fixed, separate poles cannot be correct.

Marx and Engels' argument that humanity should be understood as part of nature, rather than separate from it, is given additional force by developments in palaeoanthropology since the nineteenth century. A view that humans are somehow exceptional and therefore can or should be removed from the natural world assumes that human evolution is also separate from that of other creatures. In fact, current thinking on *Homo Sapiens'* origins emphasises how until recently (in palaeontological time) we were just one hominid species among several. Even our much-vaunted intelligence does not really set us apart, as the tendency towards bigger brains can be shown to have evolved three separate times within the hominid lineage.[87]

What is different about humans compared to other animals is not that we have an effect on the natural world around us, but that we do it consciously. We are the only living species to work for a predetermined purpose on natural materials. (But not the only dead one: our relatives *Homo Neanderthalensis* and *Homo Erectus* both made tools as well.) As Marx explained in *Capital*:

> *A spider conducts operations that resemble those of a weaver, and a bee puts to shame many an architect in the construction of her cells. But what distinguishes the worst architect from the best of the bees is this, that the architect raises his structure in imagination before he erects it in reality. At the end of every labour-process, we get a result that already existed in the imagination of the labourer at its commencement. He not only effects a change of form in the material on which he works, but he also realises a purpose of his own that gives the law to his modus operandi, and to which he must subordinate his will.*[88]

This human labour process is not necessarily damaging to the environment. Indeed, this conscious planning enables humans to consider how to carry out their operations sustainably in a way that no other animal can. Humans, for example, might decide it would be a good idea to limit the numbers of deer in a particular area to enable more saplings to grow, but the deer themselves are hardly capable of deciding not to nibble on that oak shoot because deforestation is a problem. Under capitalism, however, humans are alienated from nature.

Alienation

In capitalism, commodification means that commodity production shapes how we understand and experience the world. Workers have to sell their labour power as just another commodity, while what they produce is also just another commodity. The result of the worker's labour power appears as something alien to the worker, and the more the workers work, the more they feel cut off from what they produce. This is alienation, and since what workers are doing, either directly or indirectly, is labouring on inputs from nature, it also applies to the relation of the workers to the natural world. The more the work appropriates nature, the more the alienation from nature takes place.

Alienation is therefore the result of commodifying the natural world. It is also the case however that alienation enables continuing commodification. It is alienation that underlies the view of nature that it is simply there to be used as natural inputs as the needs of the capitalists dictate. It also shapes our view of nature in another way. As Georg Lukács pointed out, the effect of commodification is to give relationships between people the character of things: to reify them. The conception of the natural world as Nature – as an entity from which human society could feasibly be separated – can therefore be seen as part of the alienation of humans in capitalism from the natural world. After all, it can only make potential sense to talk about dividing human society from Nature if we are already alienated from nature.

For Marx and Engels, alienation from nature was a result of capitalist commodification. The conditions of industrial production, which involve driving large numbers of the rural poor into the industrial cities, were part of this alienation from nature. This was because they physically removed the bulk of the people from the countryside, setting up the division between town and country which underlay a fundamental metabolic rift. In this understanding, then, withdrawing human society still further from the natural world by segregating the world into Human and Natural areas would be the very worst thing we could do. It would be a recipe for extending, rather than tackling, alienation from nature.

Marx and Engels believed that a post-capitalist society, not based on commodity production, would be able to overcome this alienation. As Engels wrote in the *Dialectics of Nature*, as knowledge of natural processes increases in a non-capitalist society, 'the more will men not only feel but also know their oneness with nature, and thus more impossible will become and senseless and unnatural idea of a contrast between mind and matter, man and nature, soul and body ...'[89] Even if we were able, however, in an unalienated world, to make sure that our influence over the natural world did not mean environmental destruction, is it unavoidable if we don't try to limit human presence in nature?

In looking at the scale of capitalism's influence on and damage of the natural world, there can be a tendency to assume that this influence before the Industrial Revolution was negligible. It would therefore make sense to regard areas which seem to be free from the most obvious effects of industrialisation as representative of nature untouched by human society. As argued by Kozevnikov, an advocate for Russian national parks, in 1908, for example, humanity was losing 'primordial nature' through the spread of industrialisation, unless measures were implemented to set aside areas where nature could be left alone.[90] This view however involves a considerable underestimate of the degree to which pre-industrial, pre-capitalist human societies shaped the environment around them.

Non-capitalist societies and the natural world

It is well known that Western explorers and settlers had a tendency to dismiss the civilisations of non-Western peoples, particularly if, like those of the First Nations peoples in the Americas, or Aboriginal cultures in Australia, they were not easily understood as looking like the towns and cities of Europe. The usual argument was that the pre-colonial inhabitants merely lived there without affecting the natural world. Thus, for example, Thomas Mitchell, exploring the Australian bush in the early nineteenth century, described 'a beautiful plain ... [with] the appearance of an extensive park' but could not entertain the thought that this appearance could have anything to do with Aboriginal land management, viewing the trees and shrubs as only 'dropt in nature's careless haste.'[91]

As Bruce Pascoe points out in the case of Australia, this denial to native people of any influence on the natural world was an important strategy for the colonialists, forming part of an argument that dispossessing the original inhabitants was fair, since they weren't making any proper use of it anyway. In fact, there is considerable evidence that landscapes such as the Australian bush or the Amazon rainforest, which might seem prime candidates for being 'primordial wilderness', have been profoundly shaped over centuries by deliberate human activity. In Amazonia, for example, Indian land management was such that it has been claimed that 'rather than adapt to Nature, they *created* it. They were in the midst of terraforming the Amazon when Columbus showed up and ruined everything.'[92] In Australia, explorers like Mitchell were subconsciously more perceptive than they allowed themselves to be, as the landscape they were seeing was the creation of careful Aboriginal management. Mitchell *was* actually looking at a park.

The view that human influence can only damage the environment, so that the only way to save nature is to separate ourselves from it, is the result of the colonial assumption that only Western capitalist societies try to affect the natural world in any meaningful way. Since the effect of Western capitalist societies on the natural world has been generally harmful, this therefore leads to the conclusion that human effects would always be synonymous with current, capitalist ones. A reassessment of the ways in which pre-capitalist societies interacted with the natural world, however, shows that human influence does not have to be destructive. It just requires society to be organised around a sustainable relationship with the natural world; in other words, a system in which humans are not alienated from nature.

There sometimes appears to be a strain of anti-humanity in some arguments for the separation of humans from nature. It is certainly the case that historically, concern for the preservation of 'primordial nature' has been used as a tactic against people who were regarded as undesirable. British colonial authorities, for example, used the excuse that Maasai herds were bad for biodiversity as an excuse for trying to drive them out of the Serengeti.[93] Nazi attempts to create a great wilderness in the Białowieża forest involved the expulsion or murder of thousands of people and the destruction of more than 300 villages.[94] This is not of course to argue that rewilding is necessarily a fascist or colonialist endeavour. The sometimes dubious history of rewilding does show however how necessary it is to consider where an argument that humanity is fundamentally undesirable can lead.

Two gardens

At the heart of the debate about humanity's proper relation to nature are two views on the garden. The first is Malthus' description of increasing agricultural production in Britain to keep pace with an increasing population: 'in a few centuries, it would make every acre of land in the island like a garden.'[95] This is clearly a dystopian vision for Malthus; the idea that there would be nowhere in Britain unoccupied by the rural poor and their cottage gardens. The second, contrasting view is provided by William Morris in his utopian *News from Nowhere*, imagining an England long after a successful revolution. This England 'is now a garden, where nothing is wasted and nothing is spoilt, with the necessary dwellings, sheds and workshops scattered up and down the country, all trim and neat and pretty.'[96]

In Morris' vision, since this is a planned garden and not the uncontrolled result of population explosion, there are 'wilder' areas like the Forest of Dean and the New Forest, which Malthus was presumably imagining would have been grubbed up to make more space for cottages. In general, however, Morris' idea of a utopian England does sound remarkably like Malthus' vision of Hell. The difference is not in the degree of space for wilderness each writer was imagining would have been left. It is clearly the case that there would always need to be habitat for species which cannot live close to human settlements, although that's not the same as saying that those species need space preserved from human influence. The difference lies not in the limits of the imagined garden, but in what we think of it: whether a landscape shaped by human society is inherently undesirable or not. Malthus would have argued that he did not deplore poor people's existence, merely their improvidence, but his dislike of too many working-class people comes off every page of the *Principle of Population*. Morris, on the other hand, thought that without the environmental damage inherent to capitalism, all of us could and should live in a garden.

Human management of the natural world was not invented under capitalism, nor does it have to be environmentally damaging. We have in fact plenty of evidence that societies which are not alienated from nature have been able to manage the natural world in a sustainable way, from the creation of the super-fertile *terra praeta* soil in the Amazon, to controlled burning to avoid large-scale destructive wildfires in the Australian bush. That this seems impossible to replicate even in a future, imagined society is testament to capitalism's ability to make historical phenomena, like alienation, appear as part of the intrinsic human condition.

It is only because we are alienated from nature that it is possible to argue against seeing humanity as inherently part of the natural world. Seeing this as 'homocentrism' to be overcome is an alienated position. Proposals to separate human society from the natural world may seem a logical extension of current nature reserves and therefore as the only option to preserve species from destruction. Dividing the world into Human and Natural areas would however be to lock in the alienation that caused the threat of destruction in the first place. Just as serious, the process of compelling that dividing would be likely to bring out all the worst aspects of the type of green thinking which regards ordinary people as the object, rather than part of the movement.

Chapter Six: The importance of theory

The understanding that capitalism is inherently destructive of the environment requires us to frame possible responses to the climate crisis in systematic terms. This means that our efforts have to be concentrated on the systemic rather than proximate causes of destruction. As discussed, there is little value cajoling people about the harm caused by their individual lifestyles while the effect of those lifestyles is not by their personal choices. The aim has to be to change the system; changing consumer choices within it is of lesser importance.

The past and the next environmental crises
It is also important to understand that there is a difference between recognising that environmental crisis is part and parcel of the capitalist system and concluding that there is nothing to be done within capitalism to ameliorate its effects. It is clear that while the mechanisms of capitalism are the ultimate cause of environmental destruction, it is possible to find proximate solutions to individual aspects of this destructiveness, even while the inherent tendency goes on to find new ways to harm the natural world.

In this way, for example, the smog that plagued London and other cities in the UK because of coal fires was largely prevented by the Clean Air Act (1956), although we now face different air pollution problems because of emissions from traffic. The destruction of the ozone layer appears to have been successfully reversed as a result of the global bans on CFCs, at the same time as greenhouse-gas emissions are causing the climate crisis. The next looming environmental disaster would appear to be the collapse of insect populations. Across Europe and North America, nearly half of all insect species are in decline and a third are facing extinction, probably because of pesticide use and habitats lost to industrial agriculture.[97]

The solutions to the insect apocalypse are theoretically implementable within the current system, with changes to agricultural practices. In the same way, systemic changes to address the climate crisis could be implemented by governments within the capitalist system, such as the creation of green power-generation infrastructure, promotion of public transport and rail freight over private cars and lorries, and so on. Capitalism's effect on the environment is yet another reason why we need to overthrow the entire system, but there are reformist goals like these for which we can and should be fighting in the immediate term.

The fight for action on the climate crisis in these ways is an obvious part of campaigns against the neoliberal agenda of austerity and privatisation. Green new-deal proposals, for example, combine anti-austerity measures to provide good, new jobs with the necessary work to create green infrastructure. An understanding of the climate crisis as the product of capitalism's inherent tendency to environmental destruction leads not only to the conclusion that the system must be overthrown, but to immediate alliances with those who are fighting against the worst effects of the system in the here and now.

This does not mean however that all forms of concern about the climate crisis will automatically lead to reformist or left-wing conclusions. As the climate crisis has moved up the political agenda, it has become increasingly apparent that concern for the environment is not inherently politically progressive. It is not the case that more political prominence for climate issues will automatically be to the benefit of working people; or, indeed, to effective action on the climate crisis.

Right-wing populism and climate-change denial

Political responses to the climate crisis take different forms. In some places, the identification of climate change as a middle-class concern has enabled populist right-wing leaders to use climate-change denial as a way of appealing to disenfranchised, working-class voters. This was, for example, where Trump was coming from when he repudiated the Paris agreement on the basis that it would cost US manufacturing jobs. Trump's statement that he was on the side of Pittsburgh not Paris provoked a perfect comeback from the Mayor of Pittsburgh, that the city was committed to its carbon-reduction programme and voted 80% for Hillary Clinton.[98] It was nevertheless part of a strategy from the Trump administration to present themselves as the defenders of blue-collar workers against the liberal elite. Australian Prime Minister Scott Morrison's stunt of brandishing a lump of coal in a parliamentary debate in 2017 was presumably intended to have the same sort of effect. It was certainly a pose as the defender of jobs in the fossil-fuel industry against those emotional and irrational greens who believe in the reality of climate change. 'This is coal, it won't hurt you', he is reported to have said.[99] These sorts of positions are also adopted by some on the far-right, with Germany's AFD, for example, taking a climate-denial position on the basis of defending jobs in mining and other industries.[100]

This is possible political positioning only to the extent that concern about the climate crisis is seen as the preserve of the middle class to the exclusion of working people. The answer, clearly, is that campaigning on climate change needs to be rooted in working-class communities, particularly through developing concrete plans for a just transition with trades unions and other organisations. This is however untenable if we take the view that the current ecological crisis is in some way the fault of working-class people and that the only hope for the natural world is to separate them from it.

The use of the climate crisis by the Right

The adoption of climate-change denial by populists like Trump is clearly a barrier to effective action on climate change. Just as troubling, though, is the potential for the reality of climate change to be used in the service of right-wing policies. An example of this potential was the fuel tax rise proposed by France's President Macron, which sparked the *Gilet Jaunes* protests. The rise was referred to as a carbon tax, thereby attempting to justify it on climate grounds. This was widely seen as an excuse and not a reason. Protestors pointed out that only 20% of the tax was actually intended to go to projects to encourage cleaner energy. In any case, without improvements in public transport, the tax could hardly work as an incentive towards less individual fuel use. Drivers without any other option would simply have to fund the extra costs of their necessary journeys.[101]

The resistance to the fuel tax rise importantly avoided rejection of action on climate change, with various examples of *Gilet Jaunes* and climate protestors joining forces.[102] As Danièle Obono of La France Insoumise points out, the *Gilet Jaunes* protestors insist that 'economic justice and climate justice are the same fight.'[103] This insistence meant that the lesson of the protests was clearly 'not that climate action is politically toxic, but that coupling it with austerity and handouts to the one percent — failing to place blame on the corporate executives who deserve it — is a recipe for planetary disaster.'[104] Macron's attempt to use the climate crisis as a justification for an unpopular policy, and to follow it up by accusing the protestors of ignorance about climate change, remains however as an indication of the uses to which the climate crisis can be put.

Understanding the climate crisis as the responsibility of individuals clearly has much illiberal potential. It is obvious that if you see the source of the problem as people's personal choices, then given the urgency of the situation, if they cannot be persuaded to make different choices, then maybe they have to be compelled. Carbon rationing proposals, like calls to ban meat consumption, are fringe rather than part of mainstream green campaigning, but they represent the logical endpoint of a failure to see the problem and potential solutions in systematic terms.

Eco-fascism and the anti-immigration green movement
Espousing a view of human interaction with the natural world that aims to limit it as far as possible can also lead to a dangerous political place. This is demonstrated by the rise of eco-fascism. In March 2019, the shooter who murdered fifty people at two mosques in Christchurch, New Zealand, left a manifesto which included eco-fascist themes. In August, the murderer of 22 people in a Walmart in El Paso, Texas, also made explicitly eco-fascist statements in his manifesto.[105]

To some extent, this is an expression of the resurgence of the Nazi Volkish 'blood and soil' ideology, which was all about promoting a pure, honestly Germanic lifestyle in the country as opposed to the corruption of town life. This use of an idealised version of life on the land to criticise the dominant culture as decadent has a very long history. Arguably, Nazi ideas of the noble German race go all the way back to Tacitus' counterposing of the Germans and Britons against decadent Romans in the first century AD. Tacitus' Germans are very much noble savages - they don't 'find vice amusing, or [call] it up to date to debauch or be debauched'[106] - and their virtue appears to be because they are sprung from the land on which they live. They are, Tacitus says, 'natives of the soil and extremely little affected by immigration'.[107]

It is easy to see how this ideology fits into modern far-right positions on immigration, but on the face of it has little to do with modern environmentalism. It is clear, however, that while eco-fascism is explicitly neo-Nazi, it also does take in elements from green thinking. The El Paso shooter wrote in his manifesto, for example, that 'If we can get rid of enough people, then our way of life can become more sustainable.'[108] Here, of course, this is a justification for mass murder, not a prescription of contraception, but the underlying premise, that the environmental problem is that there are too many people, could have come from much of the mainstream climate movement.

The argument that the size of the population is the key environmental problem has often had a racist edge to it, as for example in the famous passage by Paul Ehrlich in his influential *The Population Bomb*, describing how a family trip to Delhi convinced him of the reality of overpopulation:

> *The streets seemed alive with people. People eating, people washing, people sleeping, people visiting, arguing and screaming ... People, people, people, people. As we moved through the mob, hand horn squawking, the dust, noise, heat and cooking fires gave the scene a hellish aspect. Would we ever get to our hotel? All three of us were, frankly, frightened ... since that night, I've known the feel of overpopulation.'[109]*

This racist association of overpopulation with too many black people arguably leads to the connection sometimes made between immigration and the climate crisis. The argument, based in the simplistic view that the greenhouse-gas emissions from each country are simply the greenhouse-gas emissions of each resident multiplied by the size of the population, is that immigration from the Third to the First world is a cause of climate crisis. Since this population movement involved moving from countries with low per-capita emissions to higher ones, immigration therefore represents an inexcusable increase in personal greenhouse-gas emissions. (Strangely, there does not appear to be anyone making the obvious corollary, that in order to reduce our per-capita emissions, we should encourage individuals in the First World to emigrate to Third World countries.) It is this use of climate change as a justification for opposing immigration which has seen some UK far-right supporters sporting Extinction Rebellion stickers.

The importance of theory

This, then, is why ecological theory matters. The actions by the youth climate strikers and by Extinction Rebellion have pushed the climate crisis up the agenda. The audience for debate on green ideas is incomparably larger than it was even in the runup to the climate summits at Copenhagen or Paris. It is also clear though that the sort of action we fight for will be determined by our understanding of what the causes of the climate crisis are. The new climate campaigns have been unspecific about this, and similarly unspecific about the action required to address the crisis. At some point, however, we will have to move from a position of simply calling for action to setting out our vision of how we could get to a post-climate-crisis world.

It is here that our theory of how environmental destruction comes about has material consequences. If the general consensus is allowed to become that climate change is the fault of selfish individuals making bad choices, this will then serve as a justification for policies aimed at nudging or compelling those individuals into 'better' choices. If we conclude that humans are an over-numerous plague on the natural world, then restrictions on population movement and population growth would be an obvious outcome. In either case, the possibilities for blaming working-class people, for using the climate crisis as an excuse to attack jobs and living conditions, is clear. The potential for the climate crisis to be weaponized by the elite is real.

Understanding environmental destruction as a systemic problem of capitalism is a starting point for a different way to deal with the climate crisis. It can underpin campaigning for things like a just transition to a sustainable infrastructure, for accessible and affordable public transport, for improved housing stock to reduce domestic emissions. Importantly, these sorts of demands would improve working people's lives now. Restoration of rural bus services, for example, would be a real benefit to large numbers of people even if we weren't facing a climate crisis. They are campaigns which we can build in working-class communities, not at or despite working-class people.

These are immediate responses to the current environmental crisis, but we have to fight for them in the clear understanding that capitalism will go on throwing up environmental crises until it is overcome. That a future, non-capitalist society could live sustainably as part of the natural world is shown by Marx and Engels' analysis of how capitalism works on the environment. It is not that humanity is inherently bad for nature; it is that capitalism runs on alienation and destruction. Without capitalism, we could all live, sustainably, in a garden.

Notes

1. Chris Goodall, *How to Live a Low-carbon Life*, (Routledge, London 2007), p.3.

2. Michael Mann, 'Lifestyle Changes Aren't Enough To Save The Planet. Here's What Could', *Time*, (12th September 2019), https://time.com/5669071/lifestyle-changes-climate-change/.

3. Aaron Bastani, *Fully Automated Luxury Communism*, (Verso, London 2019).

4. https://www.half-earthproject.org/.

5. Karl Marx and Frederick Engels, *Manifesto of the Communist Party*, (Progress Publishers, Moscow 1986), p.67.

6. For a recent summary and refutation of these accusations, see John Bellamy Foster and Paul Burkett, *Marx and the Earth. An anti-critique*, (Haymarket, Chicago 2016).

7. See for example Joel Kovel, 'The Future will be Ecosocialist', *Ecosocialist Horizons*, (25th November 2011), http://ecosocialisthorizons.com/2011/11/the-future-is-ecosocialist/.

8. Karl Marx, *Capital. A Critique of Political Economy*, vol.3, (Foreign Languages Publishing House, Moscow 1959), chapter 47, p.793.

9. Allan Chase, *The Legacy of Malthus. The Social Costs of the New Scientific Racism*, (University of Illinois Press, Chicago 1975), p.72.

10. E J Hobsbawm and George Rudé, *Captain Swing*, (Lawrence & Wishart, London 1969), p.6.

11. Marx, *Capital*, vol.1, chapter 25, p.692.

12. Justus von Liebig, quoted in Kohei Saito, *Karl Marx's Ecosocialism. Capitalism, Nature and the Unfinished*

Critique of Political Economy, (Monthly Review Press, New York 2017), p.197.

13. Liebig, quoted in Saito, *Karl Marx's Ecosocialism*, p.198.

14. https://web.archive.org/web/20141213114830/ http://www.parliament.uk/business/publications/ parliamentary-archives/archives-highlights/archives-parliament-and-the-thames/.

15. Karl Marx, 'Herr Vogt', *Collected Works*, vol.17, (Lawrence and Wishart, London 1981), p.243.

16. Peter Ackroyd, *London Under*, (Vintage, London 2012), p.80.

17. https://www.wired.co.uk/article/sewage-environment-climate-change-london.

18. https://www.museumoflondon.org.uk/discover/ how-bazalgette-built-londons-first-super-sewer.

19. See for example a recent discussion on eco-toilets: https://www.theguardian.com/global/2019/dec/09/ no-flush-movement-composting-toilet-clean-water-waste-fertiliser-eco-revolution.

20. Marx, *Capital*, vol.1, chapter 25, p.703.

21. Ibid., note 1.

22. Ibid., p.711.

23. Karl Marx, 'Outline of a Report on the Irish Question to the Communist Educational Association of German Workers in London', (1867), *Marx and Engels on Ireland*, (Progress Publishers, Moscow 1971), pp.126-139, p.136.

24. Karl Marx, 'Notes for an Undelivered Speech on Ireland', (1867), *Marx and Engels on Ireland*, pp.120-125, p.123.

25. For a detailed discussion of the guano and imperial competition over it, see John Bellamy Foster, Brett Clark and Richard York, *The Ecological Rift. Capitalism's War on the Earth*, (Monthly Review Press, New York 2010), pp.355-372.

26. Ibid., p.357.

27. AJ Duffield, *Peru in the Guano Age. Being a short*

account of a recent visit to the guano deposits with some reflections on the money they have produced and the uses to which it has been applied, (Richard Bentley and Son, London 1877), pp.77-8.

28. Bellamy Foster et al, *Ecological Rift*, p.371.

29. House of Commons Environmental Audit Committee, *UK Progress on Reducing Nitrate Pollution*, (November 2018), p.65.

30. Marx, *Capital*, vol.1, chapter 10, p.265.

31. Jason W Moore, *Capitalism in the Web of Life. Ecology and the Accumulation of Capital*, (Verso, London 2015), pp.121-2.

32. http://www.exetermemories.co.uk/em/_people/gibbs-william.php.

33. Tim Jackson, *Prosperity Without Growth? The Transition to a Sustainable Economy*, (Sustainable Development Commission 2009), p.5.

34. For a recent review of the debate, see Jason Hickel and Giorgos Kallis, 'Is Green Growth Possible?', *New Political Economy* (2019), published online at https://www.tandfonline.com/doi/full/10.1080/13563467.2019.1598964.

35. Per Espen Stoknes and Johan Rockström, 'Refining green growth within planetary boundaries', *Energy Research and Social Science* 44, (2018), pp.41-49.

36. For example https://www.theguardian.com/news/2019/dec/16/dreaming-of-a-green-christmas-heres-how-to-make-it-come-true.

37. Ted Nordhaus and Michael Shellenberger, *Break Through. Why We Can't Leave Saving the Planet to Environmentalists*, (Mariner Books, Boston – New York 2007), esp. pp. 157-215.

38. Giorgos Kallis, *Limits. Why Malthus Was Wrong and Why Environmentalists Should Care*, (Stanford University Press, Stanford 2019), p.121.

39. https://www.climatechangenews.com/2017/12/11/tsunami-data-consume-one-fifth-global-

electricity-2025/.

40. Brian Czech and Herman E Daly, 'In My Opinion: The Steady State Economy - What It Is, What It Entails and Connotes', *Wildlife Society Bulletin* 32 (2) (2004), pp.598-605.

41. See for example https://www.theguardian.com/commentisfree/2019/may/10/green-new-deal-economy-ecology, https://www.theguardian.com/news/2019/jun/17/is-time-to-end-our-fixation-with-gdp-and-growth and https://qz.com/1235255/our-obsession-with-gdp-will-lead-to-madness-but-there-are-alternatives/ among many others.

42. Thomas Princen, 'Consumption and Environment: Some Conceptual Issues', *Ecological Economics* 31 (1999), p.359.

43. Kallis, *Limits*, p.127.

44. Karl Marx, *Grundrisse. Foundations of a Critique of Political Economy (Rough Draft)*, (Penguin/New Left Review, London 1973), p.285.

45. Ibid., pp.286-7.

46. Kallis, *Limits*, p.121.

47. Marx, *Grundrisse*, pp.89-96.

48. For a fuller discussion, see my *Diet of Austerity. Class, Food and Climate Change*, (Zero Books, London 2015), pp.117-121.

49. Frederick Engels, 'Letter to Lange', 29th March 1865, printed in Ronald L Meek, *Marx and Engels on Malthus*, (Lawrence and Wishart, London 1953), p.82.

50. Ian Angus, *Facing the Anthropocene. Fossil Capitalism and the Crisis of the Earth System*, (Monthly Review Press, New York 2016).

51. Ibid., p.152.

52. https://climateandcapitalism.com/2015/02/08/pentagon-pollution-7-military-assault-global-climate/.

53. https://www.projectcensored.org/2-us-department-of-defense-is-the-worst-polluter-on-the-planet/.

54. J Rockström et al, 'Planetary Boundaries: Exploring the Safe Operating Space for Humanity', *Ecology and Society* 14 (2), (2009), p.32.

55. Thomas Princen, 'Consumption and Environment: Some Conceptual Issues', *Ecological Economics* 31 (1999), pp.347-63, p.348.

56. Frederick Engels, 'The Myth of Overpopulation', *Outlines of a Critique of Political Economy* (1844), reprinted in Meek, *Marx and Engels on Malthus*, p.58.

57. As discussed in John Bellamy Foster and Paul Burkett, *Marx and the Earth,* p.59.

58. Frederick Engels, *The Dialectics of Nature*, (Wellread Publications, London 2007), p.182.

59. T R Malthus, *Principle of Population*, 7th ed., (Everyman), p.6.

60. Ibid.

61. Emmanuel Le Roy Ladurie, *The Peasants of Languedoc*, trans. John Day, (University of Illinois Press, Chicago/London 1974), p.311.

62. Meek, *Marx and Engels on Malthus*, introduction, pp.16-17.

63. Frederick Engels, *The Condition of the Working Class in England*, (Penguin, London 1969), p.308.

64. Malthus, *Principle of Population*, 2nd ed., (Basil Blackwell, Oxford 1951), p.531.

65. Engels, *Condition of the Working Class*, p.117.

66. William Cobbett, *Rural Rides*, (Penguin, London 1967), p.317.

67. Amartya Sen, *Poverty and Famines: An Essay on Entitlement and Deprivation*, (Oxford University Press, Oxford 1981), p.1.

68. John Newsinger, *The Blood Never Dried. A People's History of the British Empire*, (Bookmarks 2006), pp.34-8.

69. For an excellent recent analysis of the complex causes of the famine, see Janam Mukherjee, *Hungry Bengal. War, Famine and the End of Empire*, (Hurst & Company, London 2015).

70. Gerald H Haug et al., 'Climate and the Collapse of Maya Civilization', *Science* 299, (14th March 2003), pp. 1731-5, p.1733.

71. Charles C Mann, *1491. New Revelations of the Americas before Columbus*, (Vintage, New York 2006), pp.308-12.

72. Ted Benton on Deep Ecology, quoted in https://www.counterfire.org/theory/37-theory/8550-paths-to-sustainability-the-case-of-deep-ecology.

73. https://www.theguardian.com/environment/2016/aug/29/declare-anthropocene-epoch-experts-urge-geological-congress-human-impact-earth.

74. Paul J Crutzen, 'Geology of Mankind', *Nature* 415/3, (3rd January 2002), p.23.

75. See for example Patricia MacCormack, *The A Human Manifesto. Activism for the End of the Anthropocene*, (Bloomsbury, London 2019).

76. Virginia Abernethy, 'Introduction' in Ester Boserup, *The Conditions of Agricultural Growth. The Economics of Agrarian Change under Population Pressure*, (Transaction Publishers, New Brunswick and London 2006), pp.vii-xiii, p.ix.

77. https://www.half-earthproject.org/half-earth-book/#about-the-book.

78. Tim Flannery (with Luigi Boitani), *Europe. A Natural History*, (Allen Lane, London 2018), p.312.

79. https://rewildingeurope.com/what-is-rewilding/.

80. Flannery, *Europe*, p.312.

81. See for example George Monbiot's January 2020 piece in the *Guardian*, https://www.theguardian.com/commentisfree/2020/jan/08/lab-grown-food-destroy-farming-save-planet.

82. Ian Angus, *Facing the Anthropocene. Fossil Capitalism and the Crisis of the Earth System*, (Monthly Review Press, New York 2016), p.57.

83. See John Bellamy Foster, *Marx's Ecology. Materialism and Nature*, (Monthly Review Press, New York 2000),

pp.123-6.

84. Karl Marx and Frederick Engels, 'Review of G. Fr. Daumer's The Religion of the New Age', *On Religion*, (Foreign Languages Publishing House, Moscow 1957), pp.90-96, p.95.

85. Karl Marx, 'Economic and Philosophical Manuscripts', *Early Writings*, (Penguin/New Left Review, London 1981), pp.279-400, p.328.

86. Frederick Engels, *Herr Eugen Dühring's Revolution in Science [Anti- Dühring]*, (Martin Lawrence Limited, London 1934), p.29.

87. See for example Ian Tattershall, *The Strange Case of the Rickety Cossack and Other Cautionary Tales from Human Evolution*, (Palgrave Macmillan, New York 2015).

88. Marx, *Capital*, vol.1, p.178.

89. Engels, *Dialectics of Nature*, p.183.

90. https://www.nytimes.com/2017/08/07/opinion/lenin-environment-siberia.html?smid=fb-share.

91. Bruce Pascoe, *Dark Emu. Aboriginal Australia and the Birth of Agriculture*, (Scribe, Melbourne and London 2018), p.25.

92. Mann, *1491*, p.349.

93. David Collett, 'Pastoralists and Wildlife: Image and Reality in Kenya Maasailand', David Anderson and Richard Grover (eds) *Conservation in Africa. Peoples, Policies and Practice*, (Cambridge University Press, Cambridge 1987), pp.129-48, p.143.

94. Flannery, *Europe*, p.300.

95. Malthus, *Principle of Population*, p.10.

96. William Morris, *News from Nowhere, or An Epoch of Rest, being some chapters from a utopian romance*, (Oxford University Press, Oxford 2003), p.62.

97. Francisco Sánchez-Bayo and Kris A G Wyckhuys, 'Worldwide Decline of the Entomofauna: A Review of its Drivers', *Biological Conservation* 232 (2019), pp.8-27, p.22.

98. https://www.counterfire.org/articles/opinion/19018-trump-s-climate-cynicism.

99. https://www.theguardian.com/global/video/2017/feb/09/scott-morrison-brings-a-chunk-of-coal-into-parliament-video.

100. https://www.cleanenergywire.org/news/right-wing-afd-continues-reject-man-made-climate-change-environmental-position-paper.

101. https://www.citylab.com/transportation/2018/11/french-protests-gilets-jaunes-emmanuel-macron-gas-diesel-tax/576196/.

102. As for example in Paris in December 2018 where marchers on the climate protest wore yellow vests: https://twitter.com/jacquesbaudrier/status/1071407672199667713.

103. https://www.jacobinmag.com/2019/05/france-insoumise-european-parliament-climate-macron.

104. https://jacobinmag.com/2018/12/yellow-vests-movement-climate-macron-cop24.

105. https://newrepublic.com/article/154971/rise-ecofascism-history-white-nationalism-environmental-preservation-immigration.

106. Tacitus, Germania, *Tacitus on Britain and Germany*, (Penguin, West Drayton 1948), p.117.

107. Ibid., p.101.

108. https://newrepublic.com/article/154971/rise-ecofascism-history-white-nationalism-environmental-preservation-immigration.

109. Paul Ehrlich, *The Population Bomb*, (Sierra Club, New York 1969), p.1. For a useful discussion of Ehrlich and his ilk, see Fred Pearce, *Peoplequake. Mass Migration, Ageing Nations and the Coming Population Crash*, (Eden Project Books, London 2010), pp.66-8.

Be part of a socialist organisation committed to fundamental change

Counterfire is a socialist organisation building the biggest possible movements against austerity, war and racism. We believe that change happens when working people get organised and fight for it. Politics is not only or mainly about what happens in parliament.

We have one of the best-read websites on the left with cutting edge news, analysis and socialist theory and we distribute thousands of copies of the left's first free paper.

Our groups meet around the country to discuss socialist politics and the developing crisis in British society and plan local action.

If you want to be part of a campaigning, revolutionary left that will fight for fundamental change then join us now.

www.counterfire.org/join